11+ tests

# 11+
## English
### Success

Age 6–7

Age 7–8

Age 8–9

Age 9–10

Age 10–11

## Assessment Papers

**Alison Head and Val Mitchell**

# Sample page

paper number for quick reference

level showing attainment target

clear instructional text

integrated mark scheme

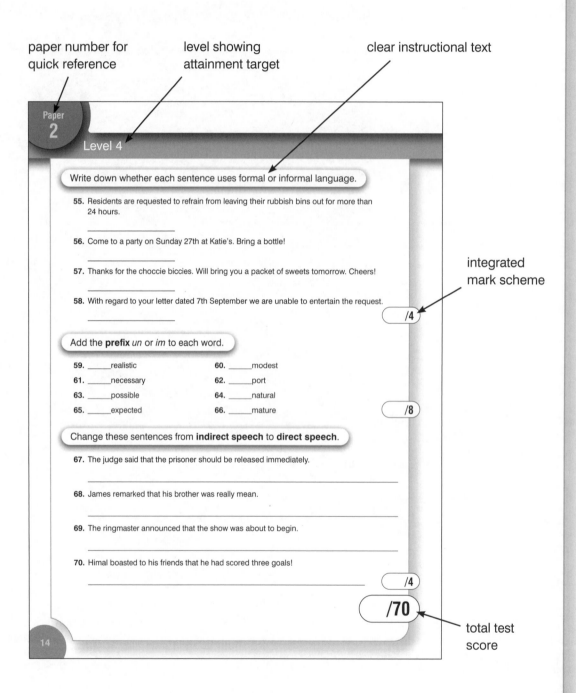

**Paper 2**

Level 4

Write down whether each sentence uses formal or informal language.

55. Residents are requested to refrain from leaving their rubbish bins out for more than 24 hours.

_____

56. Come to a party on Sunday 27th at Katie's. Bring a bottle!

_____

57. Thanks for the choccie biccies. Will bring you a packet of sweets tomorrow. Cheers!

_____

58. With regard to your letter dated 7th September we are unable to entertain the request.

_____

/4

Add the **prefix** *un* or *im* to each word.

59. _____realistic          60. _____modest

61. _____necessary        62. _____port

63. _____possible          64. _____natural

65. _____expected         66. _____mature

/8

Change these sentences from **indirect speech** to **direct speech**.

67. The judge said that the prisoner should be released immediately.

_____

68. James remarked that his brother was really mean.

_____

69. The ringmaster announced that the show was about to begin.

_____

70. Himal boasted to his friends that he had scored three goals!

_____

/4

**/70**

total test score

14

2

**PAPER 1**

### Mary Seacole, 1805–1881

1 **Mary Seacole was a pioneering nurse who overcame prejudice to play a crucial role in the Crimean War. Her story is one of extraordinary determination and bravery.**

2 Mary was born in the West Indies on her mother's home island in 1805. Her mother was Jamaican and her father was a Scottish soldier. Although, as a mixed-race woman, she would not have been enslaved, she would not have been able to vote, hold public office or become a professional either.

3 Her mother was a nurse, treating people with local herbal remedies, and Mary would play at nursing her toys and pets. By the age of 12, she was working alongside her mother.

4 Mary travelled a great deal, which would have been very unusual for a woman in those days. After travelling to London, she added European nursing techniques to her own medical knowledge. When she returned to Jamaica she took over the running of her late mother's hotel in which she often took care of sick and injured soldiers and their families.

5 In 1853 the Crimean War began. Mary decided that she wanted to help the British soldiers who were fighting against the Russians and again travelled to England to offer her services as a nurse. She hoped to work in one of the hospitals being run in Turkey by Florence Nightingale, but her applications for work were turned down again and again. Undeterred by this discrimination, Mary paid for her own passage to Turkey. However, on her arrival, she discovered that Florence Nightingale's hospitals were three day's sailing away from the fighting, so Mary decided she would find a way to help closer to the battlefields.

6 Two years after the start of the Crimean war, using her own money, she opened the new *British Hotel*, very close to the fighting in Balaclava. There she took care of sick and injured soldiers and ran a shop selling things like boots, saddles and tins of soup to the troops. She also helped on the battlefields themselves, sometimes under canon fire.

7 In 1856, at the end of the war, Mary returned to Britain with no money and in poor health. She had become very famous in Britain for her work and had many supporters there, including the Prince of Wales. They raised money for her and she wrote a best-selling book about her life called *The Wonderful Adventures of Mrs Seacole in Many Lands*. She died in 1881 and is buried in London.

Underline your answers.

1. In which section of a library would you find this text?

geography     biology        English         history

2. Where was Mary Seacole born?

Scotland      Turkey        Jamaica       Western Samoa

3. In what year did Mary Seacole open the new *British Hotel*?

1805          1853           1855           1856

/3

Answer these questions.

**4–5.** Suggest two reasons why people would have been prejudiced against Mary Seacole.

_____

_____

6. Which phrase in **paragraph** 5 suggests that Mary applied to work in the Turkish hospitals more than once.

_____

**7–8.** Suggest one advantage and one disadvantage of situating Florence Nightingale's hospitals three days away from the fighting.

advantage:      _____

disadvantage:   _____

**9–10.** Find one piece of evidence that demonstrates that Mary Seacole was brave and one piece that demonstrates that she was determined.

brave:          _____

determined:     _____

11. By the end of the Crimean War, Mary Seacole had lost all of her money. Find one piece of evidence to suggest that at the beginning of the war she would have been quite a wealthy woman.

_____

**12.** Why do you think Mary Seacole's book was a bestseller?

_____

**13.** Underline the pair of words from the text that show Mary refused to be put off by adversity.

undeterred    determination

enslaved    professional

unusual    famous

pioneering    prejudice

**14.** Tick the sentences that suggest Mary Seacole did not behave like other women of her time.

Mary Seacole was a pioneering nurse.

She would not have been enslaved.

She would not have been able to vote.

Mary travelled a great deal.

**15.** Using the text, list all the destinations Mary travelled to in chronological order, after the age of 12.

_____

_____

**16.** Read the first **paragraph** again and write down the **adjectives** that demonstrate the writer's viewpoint.

_____

**17.** Write down two points from the text that show women in Mary Seacole's time didn't have the same rights as they do in the present day.

_____

_____

**18.** Rewrite the title of Mary Seacole's book for a present-day audience.

_____     /15

Look at the organisation of the text and decide where these additional **paragraphs** should be placed. Underline your answers.

**19.** *During 1854 Mary Seacole arrived, looking for a suitable place to work. Deciding on the village of Kamara, she organised the collection of unwanted wood, packing crates and sheet metal together with old windows and door frames to rebuild an old hotel to help the soldiers.*

   After paragraph…

   4                 5                 6                 7

**20.** *Since her death Mary Seacole has been honoured both in England and in the Caribbean. An English Heritage blue plaque was erected by the Greater London Council at her residence in 157 George Street, Westminster on 9 March 1985. 110 years after her death, she was honoured in her home country with the Order of Merit.*

   After paragraph…

   4                 5                 6                 7

/2

Underline the **main clause** in each **complex sentence**.

**21.** My sister broke her ankle when she went skiing.

**22.** Because she had forgotten her bus money, Sarah had to walk home.

**23.** Amy got up early to make sure she would not be late.

**24.** Robbie waited in his classroom until the teacher was ready to speak to him.

**25.** After she had made sure it was safe, Ella crossed the road.

**26.** Max finished his project before he started his homework.

/6

Add the missing vowel to each word.

**27.** _____ny                          **28.** auth_____r

**29.** comp_____tition               **30.** _____nough

**31.** diff_____rent                   **32.** qual_____fy

**33.** ed_____ble                      **34.** fact_____ry

/8

Underline the correct use of the **verb** in brackets to complete each sentence.

**35.** The soldiers (fought  fights  will fight) bravely at the battle of Balaclava.

**36.** Travelling around Europe (was  were  is) unusual in the 19th century.

**37.** Some nurses (assisting  assisted  assist) on the battlefield in the time of Mary Seacole.

**38.** Mary Seacole, a brave nurse, was (award  awarding  awarded) a medal.

**39.** The children were (takes  taken  taking) to the exhibition.

**40.** Once we've (finish  finishing  finished) our picnic, we will pack up our rubbish and take it home.

/6

Add the **suffix** to each word, making any necessary changes to spelling.

**41.** commit + ed = _____

**42.** fit + ing = _____

**43.** ripen + ing = _____

**44.** achieve + able = _____

**45.** brave + ly = _____

**46.** big + est = _____

**47.** develop + ed = _____

**48.** rely + able = _____

/8

Underline the correct word in brackets to begin each sentence sensibly.

**49.** (Dark  Darkly  Darkness) trees provided the hunters with cover.

**50.** (Amazement  Amazingly  Amazing), I found some change in my coat pocket.

**51.** (They  We  He) tumbled out of the bouncy castle before he could catch them.

**52.** (Lovely  Quick  Carefully) balancing the glasses on a tray, she walked up the steps.

**53.** (Game  Games  Gaming) of football occur every Saturday morning at 10.30.

**54.** (Neither  Never  None) the blue team nor the yellow team won a match on Friday.

/6

Write down an **antonym** for each word.

**55.** innocent  _____

**56.** find  _____

**57.** freeze  _____

**58.** understand  _____

**59.** subtract  _____

**60.** wide  _____

**61.** ascent  _____

**62.** stale  _____

/8

Add the missing commas to these sentences.

**63–64.** We added sweetcorn onion pepper and mushrooms to our pizza.

**65–67.** I went to the cinema with Jack Mark Andrew Martin and Joe.

**68–70.** The train stopped at Reading Bristol Bath Taunton and Yeovil.

/8

/70

## PAPER 2

### Tides

I watch children play in their holes in the sand      1
In this magical place, between sea and land.
A racing car, a submarine,
anything possible they can dream.
And then I send in my foam-frilled potion      5
to take their hole back to the ocean.

Called by the moon to behave in this way
Washing the beach with my waves twice a day,
Removing all traces of splendid sandcastles
and stealing the crumbs from the folk, who with parcels   10
Of filled rolls and cakes and flasks of tea
Picnic on the beach and gaze out to sea.

The beach, please remember, belongs just to me,
and I'll take it, whenever I choose, to the sea.
Hiding my treasures in blankets of weeds      15
deep down in the depths where the sea creatures feed
I clean and I polish them smooth, bright and new,
Then lend them again to children like you.

### Underline your answers.

**1.** Where is the hole described in line 1?

under the sea    on the beach    on the moon    in a playground

**2.** How many times does the tide come in each day?

× 1 per day     × 2 per day     × 1 per week    × 2 per week

**3.** Who does the poem say the beach belongs to?

the folk      the moon      the tides      the children

/3

Answer these questions.

**4.** List three things the children build on the beach.

_____

**5.** Why might they find it a 'magical place' (line 2)?

_____

**6.** What does the poem say causes the tides?

_____

**7.** Find and copy an example of a **metaphor** in the first stanza.

_____

**8.** Find and copy an example of **alliteration** in the second stanza.

_____

**9.** What important job does the poem say that the tide does?

_____

_____

**10.** Underline the word closest in meaning to 'traces' (line 9).

troughs          evidence          drawings          memories

**11.** This poem is written in the first person. Who or what is the narrator?

_____

**12.** Underline the correct rhyming pattern for the first stanza of this poem.

AABBAB          AABBCC          ABBCDD          AAABBB

**13.** Look at the first two lines of the second stanza. Underline the correct number of syllables.

9, 9          9, 10          10, 10          11, 11

**14.** Underline the words that show **personification** in the last stanza.

whenever, again     smooth, new     children, the beach     I clean, I polish

**15.** Find an example of **assonance** in the last stanza.

_____

**16.** How do you know that this poem is written in the 20<sup>th</sup> or 21<sup>st</sup> century?

_____

**17.** What evidence is there in the last stanza that the narrator likes the children.

_____

_____

**18.** Find two **verbs** in the second stanza that suggest the narrator is a thief.

_____    _____

**19.** Find two **adjectives** in the last stanza that describe properties of the treasure.

_____    _____

**20.** From the description in stanza 2, what is the likely packaging for the picnic? Underline your answer.

a hamper        a cool box        paper wrapping        a biscuit tin

/17

> Underline the correct **homophone** to complete each sentence.

**21.** The girls had (there  their) hair cut.

**22.** '(Wear  Where) are you going?' asked Dad.

**23.** I was (too  to) full to finish my ice-cream.

**24.** (Their  There) is going to be a solar eclipse next week.

**25.** Sally couldn't decide (which  witch) shoes to wear.

**26.** My friends are great because (their  they're) lots of fun.

**27.** Our dog hides (its  it's) toys behind the sofa.

**28.** I don't (no  know) where my coat is.

/8

Sort the words into the chart.

**29–40.**  laughter    giggle    funny    from    amusingly    they

happy    cheerfully    us    see    sea    beyond

| noun | adjective | verb | adverb | pronoun | preposition |
|---|---|---|---|---|---|
|  |  |  |  |  |  |
|  |  |  |  |  |  |

/12

Underline the **onomatopoeia** in these sentences.

**41.** We warmed ourselves by the roaring fire.

**42.** The pile of boxes fell over with a crash.

**43.** The tissue paper rustled as I unwrapped the present.

**44.** The speeding car came to a screeching halt.

**45.** Rain pattered on the umbrella.

**46.** The baby gurgled happily in its pram.

/6

Write down a **synonym** for each word.

**47.** lost _____  **48.** funny _____

**49.** throw _____  **50.** dirty _____

**51.** follow _____  **52.** elegant _____

**53.** answer _____  **54.** grumpy _____

/8

Write down whether each sentence uses formal or informal language.

**55.** Residents are requested to refrain from leaving their rubbish bins out for more than 24 hours.

_____

**56.** Come to a party on Sunday 27th at Katie's. Bring a bottle!

_____

**57.** Thanks for the choccie biccies. Will bring you a packet of sweets tomorrow. Cheers!

_____

**58.** With regard to your letter dated 7th September we are unable to entertain the request.

_____

/4

Add the **prefix** *un* or *im* to each word.

**59.** _____realistic　　　　**60.** _____modest

**61.** _____necessary　　　　**62.** _____port

**63.** _____possible　　　　**64.** _____natural

**65.** _____expected　　　　**66.** _____mature

/8

Change these sentences from **indirect speech** to **direct speech**.

**67.** The judge said that the prisoner should be released immediately.

_____

**68.** James remarked that his brother was really mean.

_____

**69.** The ringmaster announced that the show was about to begin.

_____

**70.** Himal boasted to his friends that he had scored three goals!

_____

/4

/70

## PAPER 3

### Letter 1

LITTLE WITTERING 59624

THE CEDARS
27 PARKVIEW
LITTLE WITTERING
OXFORDSHIRE

My Dear Agatha,

1 You cannot imagine with what sadness I heard of the death of dearest Arthur. Naturally I was aware that he had been in failing health for some time and I had, of course, fully intended to visit you both in the crumbling rectory. However, you cannot know how busy my little brood of two keeps Brian and me.

2 Indeed, Uncle did himself write to me, imploring me to relieve you of your nursing duties for a short while, to give you a chance to rest. I smiled to myself at his misunderstanding of my situation here. As if I could leave my home here to run all by itself! A housekeeper and governess are all very well, but without my tireless attention, I swear we would all descend into chaos in no time at all. I am certain dear Uncle knew that I have always been just as devoted to his care and well-being as you.

3 Still, I suppose now you can have all the rest that you want.

4 Dear sister, I hate to think of you alone in that huge, gloomy house, filled all around by Uncle's treasures. I am sure that it must make you feel his loss all the more to be always surrounded by his books, sculptures and paintings, however valuable they may be.

5 Knowing me to be a devoted niece I am certain he would have wanted me to share in the burden of caring for some of his more valuable possessions. That is not to say, of course, that he would not want you to benefit in some small way for your nursing of him for the past 36 months. It is just that as the elder sister I may naturally expect a significant inheritance.

6 I beg you to send me a speedy reply.

Yours always,

Bella

## Letter 2

Slaughter and Dempsey Solicitors
17 Craven Mews
Hexham-on-Thames
Oxfordshire

August 20th

**Ref:** JAE/APA1

**The estate of Arthur P. Armstrong**

Dear Ms Somerton-Smythe

1 I am replying to your letter concerning the estate of Arthur Armstrong on behalf of my client Ms Agatha Armstrong, and as sole executor of your late uncle's will.

2 Ms Armstrong is, as you will understand, consumed with grief following recent events and has charged me with dealing with all general administration.

3 Due to the extensive cataloguing task being undertaken at the Rectory by your sister, it will be a number of weeks before we can give further details to answer your enquiry. We are sure you will understand the reasons for this delay.

Yours sincerely,

J Anthony Edgerton

### Underline your answers.

**Questions 1–16 are about Letter 1.**

**1.** What relation was Arthur to Bella?

father      uncle      brother      brother-in-law

**2.** How long had Agatha been nursing Arthur?

2 years      3 years      4 years      5 years

**3.** How many people are mentioned in the letter?

3      5      7      8

/3

Answer these questions.

**4.** Looking at the language used, do you think this letter was written recently, or a long time ago? Give a reason for your answer.

_____

_____

**5.** Bella says that she was just as devoted to Arthur's care as Agatha was. Do you think this is true? Give a reason for your answer.

_____

_____

**6–7.** Which two people are employed to help Bella to run her home?

_____   _____

**8.** Do you think Bella could have found the time to visit Arthur and Agatha?

_____

**9.** Which of the two sisters is the older?   _____

**10.** Do you think Arthur was a wealthy man? Find evidence in the letter to support your answer.

_____

_____

**11.** What does the word 'inheritance' mean (**paragraph** 5)?

_____

**12.** Which sister do you think deserves to get more of Arthur's money and possessions? Give a reason for your answer.

_____

_____

**13.** What standard information is missing from the beginning of the letter?

_____

**14.** Put these **paragraph** summaries in the order that they occur in the first letter.

 **a**     Bella's inability to help

 **b**     a quick response needed

 **c**     regret for Uncle's death

 **d**     opportunity for Agatha to have a rest

 **e**     size of Uncle's fortune

_____

**15.** Find three **adjectives** in the letter that describe Uncle Arthur's house.

_____

**16.** Underline the pair of words from the letter that suggest Bella is an attentive relative.

| imploring | speedy |
|---|---|
| visit | attention |
| dearest | devoted |
| intended | beg |

**Questions 17–20 are about Letters 1 and 2.**

**17.** After reading Letter 2, what do you imagine Agatha's reaction to Letter 1 might have been?

_____

**18.** From reading the salutations, which letter is the more formal?    _____

**19.** Why would you expect Bella not to be satisfied by the solicitor's response?

_____

**20.** Underline the adjective that best describes Letter 2.

   attentive        dismissive        hysterical        nasty

/17

Underline the **root word** in each of these words.

**21.** submarine          **22.** localise          **23.** realise

**24.** careful          **25.** redesign          **26.** employment

**27.** measurement          **28.** transplant

/8

Write down whether each sentence is written using **active** or **passive verbs**.

**29.** The shoes were chewed by the puppy.     _____

**30.** The shed was damaged by the wind.     _____

**31.** Our teacher handed out the books.     _____

**32.** The vase was broken by my little brother.     _____

**33.** Katie scored the winning goal.     _____

**34.** The dog bit the postman.     _____     /6

Write these sentences again, adding the capital letters and punctuation.

**35–40.** when she was nine eve moved to england from france

_____

**41–44.** alis birthday is in october

_____     /10

Add a suitable **pronoun** to complete each sentence.

**45.** Alfie was kept in at break because _____ was talking in class.

**46.** Beth and I are going shopping later because _____ need new shoes.

**47.** When the boys found the chocolate cake, _____ finished it in five minutes!

**48.** The lock was stiff because _____ needed oiling.

**49.** Mum's car broke down so Dad went to collect _____ .

**50.** Claire always does her homework as soon as _____ gets home from school.

**51.** Mark was ill so his mum made _____ go to bed.

**52.** We were disappointed because the sea was too rough for _____ to go swimming.     /8

Write the **plurals** of these words.

**53.** box _____ **54.** wolf _____

**55.** bush _____ **56.** church _____

**57.** party _____ **58.** monkey _____

**59.** mouse _____ **60.** tomato _____  /8

Write these sentences, correcting the grammar
(the meaning of each sentence should be negative).

**61.** My book wasn't nowhere to be found.

_____

**62.** Jamie went to get some milk but there wasn't none left.

_____

_____

**63.** The mechanic said there wasn't nothing he could do with the car.

_____

_____

**64.** Caitlin said that she hadn't done nothing wrong.

_____  /4

Write these words again, using the correct spelling.

**65.** intrested _____ **66.** easely _____

**67.** originul _____ **68.** diffrence _____

**69.** freedum _____ **70.** genarous _____  /6

**/70**

## PAPER 4

### The biofuel debate

1 Today, most of the energy we use comes from fossil fuels like coal, oil and natural gases. These have been produced over millions of years from the remains of plants and animals. Because we are using them many times faster than they are produced, these fuels are called non-renewable and will eventually run out.

2 There is another problem with fossil fuels. To release the energy they contain they have to be burned and that is detrimental to the environment. When the fuels burn the gas carbon dioxide is made. This gas builds up in the atmosphere and keeps the heat in around the Earth, meaning the Earth gets slowly warmer. Some other gases made are pollutants which combine with water to fall as acid rain, damaging trees and the animals that live in lakes and rivers.

3 In the future, we will have to use other sources of energy. One possibility is using biofuels. These are fuels made from plants like sugar cane. Because we can keep growing new plants this type of fuel is described as renewable. We would never run out of biofuel, although just like fossil fuels, it has to be burned to release its energy.

4 However, many people are worried about biofuels because as we use so much fuel, we would need enormous areas to grow plants. Already, land that was used to grow food and large areas of forests are being cleared to grow biofuels. Some people think that this makes biofuels just as harmful to the environment as fossil fuels. They argue that instead of replacing fossil fuels with biofuels, we should try to find ways to use less fuel.

5 In addition, although it is the richest countries in the world that use the most fuel, it is the developing countries that are growing most of the biofuel crops. Many people worry that the environment in these countries is being damaged and that people there could go hungry if not enough food is grown.

6 On the other hand, growing biocrops earns some of these countries a lot of money which they could use to make life better for the people who live there.

7 Research into biofuels and other renewable energy sources, like solar, wave or wind power, continues and the debate over which is best looks set to continue. One thing is certain however: we cannot continue to rely on fossil fuels for our energy because one day they will simply not be there.

Underline your answers.

1. Fossil fuels are made from...

   coal          oil          plants and animals          biofuel

2. Which of these energy sources is non-renewable?

   solar power     wind power     wave power     natural gases

3. Which of these are sometimes cleared to grow biofuel?

   forests          towns          coal mines          sugar cane

/3

Answer these questions.

4. Why do you think fuels like coal, oil and gas are called 'fossil fuels'?

   _____

5–6. List two problems with fossil fuels.

   _____

   _____

7. Which gas, mentioned in the text, is part of the reason for the Earth getting hotter?

   _____

8. Find one thing that fossil fuels and biofuels have in common.

   _____

9. How would it help the environment if we all used less fuel, be it fossil fuel or biofuel?

   _____

   _____

10–11. Describe one possible advantage and one possible disadvantage to a developing country which grows crops to make biofuel.

   advantage:     _____

   disadvantage:     _____

**12.** Why do you think the richest countries grow less biofuels?

_____

_____

**13.** Which **connectives** at the beginning of **paragraphs** are used to introduce opposing views?

_____

**14.** Which paragraph could be introduced by the subheading 'Food or fuel?'

_____

**15.** What does the word 'detrimental' mean in paragraph 2?

_____

**16.** Underline the category of text which best describes 'The biofuel debate'.

    recount        procedural    explanatory    discussion

**17.** How does the writer include the reader in this text?

_____

_____

**18.** Underline the description which best describes 'The biofuel debate'.

    amusing        biased        balanced      persuasive

**19.** Explain your answer to question 18.

_____

_____

**20.** Underline the most likely period in which this text could have been written.

    1920s        1940s        1960s        1990s

/17

Underline the **conditional clause** in each sentence.

**21.** If it snows, we will go sledging.

**22.** Should our train be delayed, we will miss the concert.

**23.** I will move up to the next group if I pass the test.

**24.** I'll bring your book back tomorrow if I can find it.

**25.** I would have left earlier had I known the car would break down.

**26.** If I were you, I would start that piece of work again.

/6

Add the **suffix** *ible* or *able* to each word, making any necessary changes to spelling.

**27.** fashion _____

**28.** agree _____

**29.** reverse _____

**30.** sense _____

**31.** access _____

**32.** value _____

**33.** reason _____

**34.** response _____

/8

Identify the part of speech that begins each sentence, using the list below.

noun   adjective   verb   adverb   pronoun   preposition   definite article   indefinite article

**35.** The ball was kicked by Rory into the back of the net. _____

**36.** Dark trees loomed over the deserted house. _____

**37.** Jumping into her car, Mary spotted her mobile phone. _____

**38.** After tea, the boys played on the computer. _____

**39.** A blanket of snow covered the farmhouse. _____

**40.** Curry and chips is my favourite dinner! _____

/6

Underline the **root word**, then write another word that shares the same root.

**41–42.** clearly _____

**43–44.** manageable _____

**45–46.** used _____

**47–48.** friendship _____

**49–50.** lovely _____

/10

Add the speech marks to these sentences.

**51–54.** Did a letter arrive for me? asked Dad. I was expecting one yesterday.

**55–56.** Molly, yawning quietly in the back of the car, asked, Are we nearly there?

/6

Pick two **adjectives** from the list to describe each thing. You can only use each adjective once.

delicious  fluffy  destructive  exhilarating  creamy  thrilling  electric  silky

**57–58.** a fairground ride             _____  _____

**59–60.** an ice-cream sundae        _____  _____

**61–62.** a kitten's fur                   _____  _____

**63–64.** a storm                          _____  _____

/8

Add a suitable **adverb** to complete each sentence using the list. You can only use each adverb once.

politely  busily  enthusiastically  brightly  menacingly  silently

**65.** The children clapped _____ when the clowns came into the ring.

**66.** The lion bounded _____ towards the edge of its enclosure.

**67.** Bees buzzed _____ from flower to flower.

**68.** When the fire alarm sounds, we must leave the classroom _____.

**69.** The boy held the door open _____ for the man behind.

**70.** The stars twinkled _____ in the sky.

/6

/70

## PAPER 5

### Royal Theatre raises the roof

1   There's new hope for an old theatre after supporters raised enough money to repair its leaking roof. Biddecomb's Royal Theatre was built in the middle of the Victorian era (1837–1901) and was a favourite haunt of Prince Albert, but a lack of investment over the past 30 years has left the walls crumbling and the window frames rotting. However, now that a group of local supporters have raised the £500,000 needed to repair the roof, a bright future awaits.

2   Publicity manager Dawn McGrath explains, 'Local people have been fantastic and, now that we can keep the rain out, there is real hope for this beautiful old theatre. We have some great shows coming up in the next few months, including The Tempest, An Inspector Calls and the pantomime Peter Pan.'

3   The theatre also plays host to TV's Ghost Watch this Friday, when the crew will be broadcasting live from the theatre. They will be hoping to hear from Tilly Marne, who was a ballerina at the theatre in the 1930s and is said to haunt the stage area. Tilly was badly injured when some scenery fell on her during rehearsals for Sleeping Beauty and although she recuperated, she never danced again. A ballet company performing here in 1962 reportedly found their ballet shoes worn out one morning and since then people have claimed that Tilly returns to dance at night.

4   So are the TV crew in for a shock? 'Personally, I don't think so,' says Dawn. 'Tilly went on to marry her childhood sweetheart. They emigrated to Canada and lived long happy lives. In 1962 she was alive and well and running a ballet school in Vancouver. If the TV show helps to publicise the theatre though, that can only be a good thing!'

5   An exhibition of old costumes worn in performances at the theatre, including a tutu worn by Tilly Marne, is being held at the Town Hall until the end of March. When it closes, the costumes will be auctioned to raise funds to repair the decorative plasterwork.

*Glory Chapman*

**Playwright**

Underline your answers.

1. Which pantomime will play at the theatre?

   Sleeping Beauty          Peter Pan          The Tempest          Ghost Watch

2. What was Tilly Marne's job?

   inspector          publicity manager          theatre supporter          ballerina

3. When was the theatre built?

   1860s          1930s          1960s          1830s

/3

Answer these questions.

4. Why might a 'lack of investment' in an old building be a particular problem?

   _____

   _____

5. What happened to Tilly Marne in the theatre?

   _____

6. What could be another explanation for the worn out shoes, other than a dancing ghost?

   _____

   _____

7. In your own words, explain why Dawn McGrath does not think that Tilly haunts the theatre.

   _____

   _____

8. What does the word 'emigrated' mean (**paragraph** 4)?

   _____

9. Why do you think Dawn McGrath says that publicity 'can only be a good thing'?

   _____

   _____

**10.** What will happen to the costumes in the exhibition when it has finished?

_____

_____

**11.** Why do you think the newspaper article makes a special point of telling readers that Tilly Marne's tutu is appearing in the costume exhibition?

_____

_____

**12.** What parts of the theatre need repairing?

_____

_____

**13.** Underline the **paragraph** number below to which this sentence could be added.

_West End actress Jane Southall will be playing the leading role in this beloved children's pantomime._

paragraph 2     paragraph 3     paragraph 4     paragraph 5

**14.** Underline the kind of publication where you would be likely to find this text.

recipe book     local newspaper     playscript     encyclopaedia

**15.** Who is the question in paragraph 4 addressed to?

_____

**16.** What does the word 'recuperated' mean (paragraph 3)?

_____

**17.** Find an example of **alliteration** in the text.

_____

**18.** Do you think the writer of this text is a theatre goer? Give a reason for your answer.

_____

_____

**19.** Why do you think the theatre is called a 'Royal' theatre?

_____

_____

**20.** Underline the place where the Royal Theatre is most likely to be situated.

a city        a town        a village        a hamlet

/17

Add *ie* or *ei* to compete each word.

**21.** rel_____f          **22.** rec_____ve          **23.** h_____ght

**24.** bel_____ve          **25.** s_____ze          **26.** sh_____ld

/9

**27.** rec_____pt          **28.** w_____rd          **29.** ch_____f

Write a **definition** for each of these words.

**30.** fact:

_____

**31.** fiction:

_____

**32.** opinion:

_____

/3

Write down the **plurals** of these **nouns**.

**33.** calf          _____          **34.** bone          _____

**35.** pitch          _____          **36.** woman          _____

**37.** ox          _____          **38.** baby          _____

**39.** turkey          _____          **40.** gate          _____

/8

29

Write these words with the correct spelling.

**41.** goverment _____   **42.** rasberry      _____

**43.** hanbag    _____   **44.** miniture     _____

**45.** vegtable   _____   **46.** histry       _____

**47.** seprate    _____   **48.** Wenseday     _____

/8

Add a suitable **conjunction** to complete each sentence.

**49.** Mum will be angry _____ I am late home.

**50.** Our dog stayed with my auntie _____ we got back from holiday.

**51.** We bought Alex a present _____ it was his birthday.

**52.** I wanted to make a sandwich _____ we had run out of bread.

**53.** I can't go out _____ I have finished my homework.

**54.** I was eight years old _____ we moved to this town.

/6

Add a **prefix** to each word to make a new word.

**55.** _____port          **56.** _____charge

**57.** _____vision        **58.** _____scope

**59.** _____cycle         **60.** _____arrange

**61.** _____graph         **62.** _____historic

/8

Use *was* or *were* to complete each sentence.

**63.** Amy _____ busy writing a story.

**64.** The children _____ playing hockey.

**65.** A flock of birds _____ roosting in the trees.

**66.** Eve's pictures _____ all over her bedroom walls.

**67.** Because the bus was late, Ali and Sam _____ late for school.

/5

Write a second **clause** to complete these sentences.

**68.** It began to snow while _____.

**69.** I lost my bag but _____.

**70.** We brushed our teeth before _____.

/3

/70

## PAPER 6

1   As the coach drew up in the car park, it started to drizzle. The group was more than an hour late because of a jam on the motorway and the class was tired and fed up. Their guide met them and ushered them to the entrance of the caves for what she called 'the briefing'. This turned out to be a list of rules delivered to the group as they shivered in the rain, which was falling like a waterfall by then. 'Stay together, watch out for slippery surfaces and don't, under any circumstances, leave the lit route.'

2   It all sounded so obvious and boring. Like Tom's mum said, if it was dangerous they would never let children go down there.

3   Inside the cave, things were a bit better. They were out of the pelting rain at least. Every now and then a spotlight would pick out a stalactite or other geological feature and the guide would pause to explain how it had formed. Lingering at the back of the group, and already restless from the dreadful journey, the boys soon lost interest. They shone their torches into side passages and caverns and up into their faces to make them look scary.

4   Busily making shadow figures on the walls of the cave, the boys didn't notice the rest of the class filing off into the next chamber. As the guide's voice faded away, they missed her explaining how the unlit outlying tunnel system frequently flooded in heavy rain. They didn't hear how, out of more than 40 tunnels in the complex, only the very narrowest led back to the surface.

5   Five minutes later, surrounded by silence, Tom realised they had been left behind. Pulling Luke and James along with him, he raced into the next chamber, skidding on the slippery surface. Inside, they were faced with three tunnels. One, although well lit with floodlights, was so narrow that you would have to turn sideways in order to pass along it.

6   'They won't have gone in there,' said Tom. 'It must be one of the others.'

7   'Let's try this one,' suggested Luke. 'There are a few emergency lights down here. We'll go a little way in, and then if we can't hear them, we'll come back and try the other one.'

8   It seemed like a good plan, but not far inside, the tunnel forked again. Only one passage was lit at all and after a few metres the lights fizzled out, and the boys decided to turn back. But then they reached another fork.

9   'It all looks different from this direction,' said James. 'Surely we should be heading back towards the surface, but all of these tunnels lead further down. We must have missed the right one, or we'd be able to hear the others.'

# English Age 10–11 Assessment Papers Answers

**PAPER 1**

1. history
2. Jamaica
3. 1855
4–5. Answers might include:
   She was a woman and also of mixed race.
6. again and again

**Answers to 7–12 might include:**

7–8. advantage: They would have been safe from the fighting./ They would have been quieter away from the fighting.
   disadvantage: It was a long way for injured men to travel.
9–10. brave: She helped the soldiers even under fire.
   determined: She decided to go to Turkey, even though she had been turned down.
11. She was able to pay for her passage to the Crimea./She set up the new *British Hotel* with her own money.
12. Because she had led a very unusual life for a woman at that time and had helped a lot of people.
13. undeterred, determination
14. Mary Seacole was a pioneering nurse.
   Mary travelled a great deal.
15. London/England, Jamaica, England, Turkey, Crimea/ Balaclava, Britain/England
16. pioneering, crucial, extraordinary
17. Two of: They could not... vote, hold public office or become a professional.
18. Answers will vary but should be less formal, for example using 'Mary' rather than 'Mrs'. An acceptable answer would be, 'The Travels of Mary Seacole'.
19. 5
20. 7

21. My sister broke her ankle when she went skiing.
22. Because she had forgotten her bus money, Sarah had to walk home.
23. Amy got up early to make sure she would not be late.
24. Robbie waited in his classroom until the teacher was ready to speak to him.
25. After she had made sure it was safe, Ella crossed the road.
26. Max finished his project before he started his homework.
27. any
28. author
29. competition
30. enough
31. different
32. qualify
33. edible
34. factory
35. The soldiers fought bravely at the battle of Balaclava.
36. Travelling around Europe was unusual in the 19th century.
37. Some nurses assisted on the battlefield in the time of Mary Seacole.
38. Mary Seacole, a brave nurse, was awarded a medal.
39. The children were taken to the exhibition.
40. Once we've finished our picnic, we will pack up our rubbish and take it home.
41. committed
42. fitting
43. ripening
44. achievable
45. bravely
46. biggest
47. developed
48. reliable

49. Dark trees provided the hunters with cover.
50. Amazingly, I found some change in my coat pocket.
51. They tumbled out of the bouncy castle before he could catch them.
52. Carefully balancing the glasses on a tray, she walked up the steps.
53. Games of football occur every Saturday morning at 10.30.
54. Neither the blue team nor the yellow team won a match on Friday.

**Answers to 55–62 might include:**

55. guilty
56. lose
57. thaw
58. misunderstand
59. add
60. narrow
61. descent
62. fresh
63–64. We added sweetcorn, onion, pepper and mushrooms to our pizza. (an optional comma could also be added after 'pepper')
65–67. I went to the cinema with Jack, Mark, Andrew, Martin and Joe. (an optional comma could also be added after 'Martin')
68–70. The train stopped at Reading, Bristol, Bath, Taunton and Yeovil. (an optional comma could also be added after 'Taunton')

**PAPER 2**

1. on the beach
2. x 2 per day
3. the tides
4. racing car/submarine/splendid sandcastles

5. Answers might include: because they can imagine all sorts of things there

6. the moon

7. foam-frilled potion

8. splendid sandcastles

9. It cleans the beach.

10. evidence

11. the tide

12. AABBCC

13. 10, 10

14. I clean, I polish

15. beach, please/sea creatures feed

16. It mentions a racing car, a submarine/flasks of tea.

17. The narrator states in the last line that it wants to lend its treasures to the children again.

18. removing, stealing

19. Two of: smooth, bright, new

20. paper wrapping

21. The girls had <u>their</u> hair cut.

22. '<u>Where</u> are you going?' asked Dad.

23. I was <u>too</u> full to finish my ice-cream.

24. <u>There</u> is going to be a solar eclipse next week.

25. Sally couldn't decide <u>which</u> shoes to wear.

26. My friends are great because <u>they're</u> lots of fun.

27. Our dog hides <u>its</u> toys behind the sofa.

28. I don't <u>know</u> where my coat is.

29–40.

| noun | adjective |
| --- | --- |
| laughter | funny |
| sea | happy |

| verb | adverb |
| --- | --- |
| giggle | amusingly |
| see | cheerfully |

| pronoun | preposition |
| --- | --- |
| they | from |
| us | beyond |

41. We warmed ourselves by the <u>roaring</u> fire.

42. The pile of boxes fell over with a <u>crash</u>.

43. The tissue paper <u>rustled</u> as I unwrapped the present.

44. The speeding car came to a <u>screeching</u> halt.

45. Rain <u>pattered</u> on the umbrella.

46. The baby <u>gurgled</u> happily in its pram.

**Answers to 47–54 might include:**

47. misplaced

48. amusing

49. hurl

50. filthy

51. chase

52. graceful

53. reply

54. cross/irritable

55. formal

56. informal

57. informal

58. formal

59. unrealistic

60. immodest

61. unnecessary

62. import

63. impossible

64. unnatural

65. unexpected

66. immature

**Answers to 67–70 might include:**

67. 'Release the prisoner immediately!' said the judge.

68. 'My brother is really mean,' remarked James.

69. 'The show is about to begin!' announced the ringmaster.

70. 'I've scored three goals!' Himal boasted to his friends.

## PAPER 3

1. uncle

2. 3 years

3. 8 people: Agatha, Uncle Arthur, Bella, two children, Brian, housekeeper, governess

**Answers to 4–5 might include:**

4. a long time ago, because the telephone number is written differently/it includes old-fashioned language, e.g. dearest Arthur, Indeed, governess

5. No, because she never found the time to visit him.

6–7. a housekeeper, a governess

8. Answers might include: Yes, because she had plenty of help to run her home.

9. Bella

10. Yes, because Bella mentions his 'treasures', 'valuable possessions' and 'significant inheritance'.

11. Something given or left to you when someone dies.

12. Answers may include: Agatha, because she took care of Uncle Arthur.

13. the date (because of the informal nature of the letter, a title and reference is not required)

14. c, a, d, e, b

15. crumbling, huge, gloomy

16. dearest, devoted

17. Answers might include: Agatha was so cross/upset that she has decided to deal with her sister through a solicitor.

18. the second letter (because it includes a reference, title and refers to the addressee formally as Ms Somerton-Smythe)

19. Answers might include: because she will have to wait a long time for any information

20. dismissive

21. sub<u>marine</u>

22. <u>local</u>ise

23. <u>real</u>ise

24. <u>care</u>ful

25. <u>redesign</u>

26. <u>employ</u>ment

27. <u>measure</u>ment

28. trans<u>plant</u>

29. passive

30. passive

31. active

32. passive

33. active

34. active

35–40. When she was nine, Eve moved to England from France.

41–44. Ali's birthday is in October.

45. Alfie was kept in at break because he was talking in class.

46. Beth and I are going shopping later because we need new shoes.

47. When the boys found the chocolate cake, they finished it in five minutes!

48. The lock was stiff because it needed oiling.

49. Mum's car broke down so Dad went to collect her/it.

50. Claire always does her homework as soon as she gets home from school.

51. Mark was ill so his mum made him go to bed.

52. We were disappointed because the sea was too rough for us to go swimming.

53. boxes

54. wolves

55. bushes

56. churches

57. parties

58. monkeys

59. mice

60. tomatoes

61. My book was nowhere to be found./My book wasn't anywhere to be found.

62. Jamie went to get some milk but there was none left./Jamie went to get some milk but there wasn't any left.

63. The mechanic said there was nothing he could do with the car./The mechanic said there wasn't anything he could do with the car.

64. Caitlin said that she hadn't done anything wrong./Caitlin said that she had done nothing wrong.

65. interested

66. easily

67. original

68. difference

69. freedom

70. generous

## PAPER 4

1. plants and animals

2. natural gases

3. forests

4. Because they are formed over millions of years from dead plants and animals.

5–6. Answers might include: They are non-renewable and burning them damages the environment.

7. carbon dioxide

8. They both have to be burned.

9. Answers might include: We would need to burn less fuel to produce the energy we need.

### Answers to 10–12 might include:

10–11. advantage: Selling biofuel crops would earn a lot of money for the country.

disadvantage: They may not have enough land to grow the biofuel crop and food to eat.

12. Because they know that they can afford to buy biofuel from other countries without needing to damage the environment in their own country.

13. However, On the other hand

14. Paragraph 5

15. causes damage/harmful

16. discussion

17. By the use of the words 'we' and 'our', so the reader feels they are included in the debate with the author.

18. balanced

19. Answers might include: The text puts different points of view in separate paragraphs and does not use emotive language.

20. 1990s

21. If it snows, we will go sledging.

22. Should our train be delayed, we will miss the concert.

23. I will move up to the next group if I pass the test.

24. I'll bring your book back tomorrow if I can find it.

25. I would have left earlier had I known the car would break down.

26. If I were you, I would start that piece of work again.

27. fashionable

28. agreeable

29. reversible

30. sensible

31. accessible

32. valuable

33. reasonable

34. responsible

35. definite article

36. adjective

37. verb

38. preposition

39. indefinite article

40. noun

### Answers to 41–50 might include:

41–42. clearly, unclear

43–44. manageable, manager

45–46. used, useful

47–48. friendship, friendly

49–50. lovely, loveable

51–54. 'Did a letter arrive for me?' asked Dad. 'I was expecting one yesterday.'

55–56. Molly, yawning quietly in the back of the car, asked, 'Are we nearly there?'

57–58. exhilarating, thrilling

59–60. creamy, delicious

61–62. fluffy, silky

63–64. destructive, electric

65. The children clapped <u>enthusiastically</u> when the clowns came into the ring.

66. The lion bounded <u>menacingly</u> towards the edge of its enclosure.

67. Bees buzzed <u>busily</u> from flower to flower.

68. When the fire alarm sounds, we must leave the classroom <u>silently</u>.

69. The boy held the door open <u>politely</u> for the man behind.

70. The stars twinkled <u>brightly</u> in the sky.

# PAPER 5

1. Peter Pan

2. ballerina

3. 1860s

4. Old buildings tend to need a lot of expensive repairs.

5. She was injured when some scenery fell on her.

6. Answers might include: The dance group had worn the shoes out themselves and never noticed.

7. Because in 1962, when people thought her ghost had worn out the ballet shoes, she was alive and well.

8. went to live in another country

9. Answers might include: If lots of people know about the theatre they will sell more tickets and raise more money.

10. They will be auctioned to raise money to repair the theatre's decorative plasterwork.

11. Answers might include: Because people will be interested in buying Tilly's tutu as a result of the ghost story that surrounds her.

12. leaking roof, crumbling walls, rotting window frames, decorative plasterwork

13. paragraph 2

14. local newspaper

15. Although the question is answered by Dawn McGrath, it is, in fact, addressed to the reader.

16. recovered

17. <u>Royal</u> Theatre <u>raises</u> the <u>roof</u> (see title)

18. Answers might include: The author is a playwright so is likely to go to the theatre.

19. Because it was a favourite place for Prince Albert to visit (and he was a member of the royal family).

20. a town (the exhibition is held in the Town Hall)

21. relief

22. receive

23. height

24. believe

25. seize

26. shield

27. receipt

28. weird

29. chief

**Answers to 30–32 might include:**

30. Something that can be shown to be true.

31. A made-up story.

32. Someone's point of view on a topic.

33. calves

34. bones

35. pitches

36. women

37. oxen

38. babies

39. turkeys

40. gates

41. government

42. raspberry

43. handbag

44. miniature

45. vegetable

46. history

47. separate

48. Wednesday

**Answers to 49–62 might include:**

49. Mum will be angry <u>if</u> I am late home.

50. Our dog stayed with my auntie <u>until</u> we got back from holiday.

51. We bought Alex a present <u>because</u> it was his birthday.

52. I wanted to make a sandwich <u>but</u> we had run out of bread.

53. I can't go out <u>before</u> I have finished my homework.

54. I was eight years old <u>when</u> we moved to this town.

55. export

56. recharge

57. revision

58. telescope

59. bicycle

60. rearrange

61. photograph

62. prehistoric

63. Amy <u>was</u> busy writing a story.

64. The children <u>were</u> playing hockey.

65. A flock of birds <u>was</u> roosting in the trees.

66. Eve's pictures <u>were</u> all over her bedroom walls.

67. Because the bus was late, Ali and Sam <u>were</u> late for school.

**Answers to 68–70 might include:**

68. It began to snow while <u>we were walking home</u>.

69. I lost my bag but <u>Dan found it again</u>.

70. We brushed our teeth <u>before we went to bed</u>.

# PAPER 6

1. a school class

2. at the cave mouth

3. three

4. drizzle

5. That if the caves were dangerous, they wouldn't let groups of children inside.

6. When it rains heavily, the tunnels flood.

7. Because it is very narrow.

8. Because they have torches.

9–10. Two of: cold, damp, hungry

**Answers to 11–12 might include:**

11. The torch would be more useful because it would enable them to see in the dark, whereas the mobile phone would not be able to get a signal underground.

12. It would be a bad idea for the boys to split up to look for a way out because it would be harder to find three boys lost separately than three together.

13. spotlight, torches, floodlights, emergency lights

14. skidding, raced

15. Answers might include: The Lost Boys, Below Ground

16. falling like a waterfall

17. paragraph 2

18. Listen to safety instructions.

19. a cliffhanger

20. car park, motorway, spotlight, mobile phone. Coach or torch are not acceptable answers: a coach could be a horse-drawn coach; a torch could be a naked flame.

21. The little girl was scratched by the cat.

22. The silence was shattered by an owl's hoot.

23. The best story was written by Tara.

24. A rockery was built in the garden by Mum.

25. The traffic was held up by roadworks.

26. The cricket match was stopped by the rain.

27. butterflies

28. children

29. geese

30. men

31. sheep

32. teeth

33–48. 'Are we nearly there?' whined Oscar.

'Not too much further,' replied Dad.

'Can we go straight to the beach when we get there?' begged Oscar.

'If you like,' laughed Dad.

**Answers to 49–54 might include:**

49. Anna was <u>pleased</u> that the holidays were over.

50. <u>Unfortunately</u>, a new road is being built to carry the extra traffic.

51. Dad is <u>selling</u> a car.

52. I am the <u>shortest</u> in my class.

53. The train to Birmingham is due to <u>leave/depart</u> at 3.15.

54. The maths homework was quite <u>easy</u>.

55. metaphor

56. simile

57. simile

58. metaphor

59. metaphor

60. simile

61–62. The twins wore <u>different</u> outfits <u>to</u> the fancy dress party.

63–64. When the performance ended, several <u>actors</u> went <u>shopping</u> for replacement costumes.

65. Under the tree, James found a new place to hide his secret letter.

66. Behind the bike sheds, there was an old World War Two pillbox.

67. Gemma broke her arm when she fell over the tree trunk.

68. Jumping and bouncing were the favourite pastimes of their new poodle, Daisy.

69. Thick fog covered the estuary.

70. Sadly, the '70s outfit was too small for Kishori.

## PAPER 7

1. Miss Smith

2. two terms

3. colouring-in and handwriting practice

4. ruining their lessons a bit at a time

5. The children feel that ruining a cover teacher's lessons is as enjoyable as eating something really delicious.

6–7. They felt a tingling/weakness behind the knees. They wriggled on the floor like slugs.

8–9. military precision, laid out in regiments

10. Answers might include: Miss Smith looks very smart and is so organised that the children find it hard to be naughty. Miss Mess is less neatly dressed, so the children may think that she will be disorganised and not be able to keep control.

11. Going straight across, from left to right, flat – like the horizon.

12. Answers might include: No, because they have always managed to spoil the lessons of other cover teachers but Miss Mess seems able to control the class in some way.

13. You would be given pink worksheet 3.2.

14. easy to manipulate

15. paragraph 4

16. past tense

17. to show how quickly Miss Smith solves problems

18. strong, effective

19. fantasy

20. A few children wriggled on the floor like slugs.

21. I <u>did</u> my homework before I watched TV.

22. When the window was broken, the girls admitted they had <u>done</u> it.

23–24. I <u>did</u> not do the washing up because I thought my sister had <u>done</u> it.

25–26. When I saw the picture that Chris had <u>done</u>, I <u>did</u> one just like it.

5

**27–41.** 'Settle down class,' said the teacher. She gave each of us a question paper, an answer paper and a sharp pencil. The teacher said, 'You have 30 minutes for the test and the time starts now.'

**42.** Our cats sleep on our beds.

**43.** My friends are eating oranges.

**44.** The roads were very busy.

**45.** My brothers are playing computer games.

**46.** The teachers collect our books.

**Answers to 47–54 might include:**

**47.** partnership

**48.** unusual

**49.** musical

**50.** comfortable

**51.** freedom

**52.** decorative

**53.** fortunate

**54.** curiosity

**55.** dance

**56.** notebook

**57.** they

**58.** Paris

**59.** massive

**60.** silently

**61.** We brought Freddie a season ticket for his birthday; he loved rugby.

**62.** Jennel bought her ingredients from the supermarket: chocolate drops, flour, margarine, milk and silver balls.

**63.** Denny: Where did I leave my glasses? (exit, stage left)

**64–66.** Under her bed, Maddie found: a mouldy apple, half eaten; a packet of peppermint chewing gum; two sugar mice with fluff all over them.

**67–68.** The wrapping paper was covered with balloons and ribbons.

**69–70.** The cake's icing was turquoise and pink with great big decorative plastic flowers.

## PAPER 8

**1.** King Aegeus

**2.** 14 (including Theseus)

**3.** Naxos

**4.** long-running dispute or argument

**5.** Answers might include: No, because he didn't want him to go in the first place, suggesting that he thought he would fail to kill the Minotaur.

**6.** He planned to use a white sail, which could be seen from Athens while his boat was still out at sea.

**7.** a maze

**Answers to 8–10 might include:**

**8.** Because if the Minotaur was lost in the labyrinth, it would be less likely to escape.

**9.** It helps him because he tied one end to the door and unravelled it as he went, so he could follow it back to the entrance later.

**10.** No, because she gives him the sword he uses to kill the Minotaur.

**11.** Because he had promised to take her with him and he was breaking this promise.

**12.** He thought that Theseus was dead when he saw the black sail and in his grief he jumped to his death in the sea.

**13.** murderers

**14.** Use a white sail.

**15.** paragraphs 1, 3, and 4 ('Long ago', 'When', 'The next morning')

**16.** b, d, a, c

**17.** distraught

**18.** black sail, ship

**19.** Long ago

**20.** bellowing/snorting

**21.** cocoa

**22.** ghost

**23.** rhyme

**24.** leopard

**25.** answer

**26.** gnaw

**27.** lamb

**28.** guitar

**29–43.** We crept through the forest, looking carefully about us. 'Look, there's one!' said Dad. We looked up and saw a red squirrel in the branches above us. It looked at us for a moment then leapt into another tree.

**44.** The theatre is near here.

**45.** I have to be back before it gets dark.

**46.** We will have enough time to finish our work.

**47.** We can have fish and chips for tea.

**48–50.** find: to locate

fined: made to pay a fee for breaking a rule/law

**51–53.** real: genuine

reel: a spool or roll of thread or line/a dance/to lurch or stagger

**54–56.** hair: strands that grow from (mammals' and marsupials') bodies

hare: an animal like a rabbit/to run about quickly

**Answers to 57–62 might include:**

**57.** 'Are you going to drama club tonight?' asked Beth.

**58.** The motorcyclists in the display team were incredible!

**59.** Creeping quietly, the fox hunted the rabbit.

**60.** The dense fog was impossible to see through.

**61.** 'That's not yours, it's mine,' wailed Mandy.

**62.** The shrivelled old man peered through the keyhole.

**Answers to 63–70 might include:**

**63–64.** within, without

**65–66.** forehead, forecast

**67–68.** international, interview

**69–70.** understand, understated

## PAPER 9

1. Burma
2. 1995
3. 54

**Answers to 4–5 might include:**

4. Because they are strong and specially adapted to moving around the terrain and can get to places the vehicles cannot, especially if roads have been damaged.
5. Because they wanted to support their country in the war.

6–7. Two of: tracking and attacking the enemy, searching for wounded, locating explosives

8. They could reach places that vehicles could not.
9. Because they were sometimes the only reliable way to get messages behind enemy lines.

**Answers to 10–12 might include:**

10. If their planes crashed or ditched, the pigeons could be sent back with details of the crew's location, so they could be rescued.

11–12. for: Animals are very loyal and may enjoy helping people.

against: Animals may be frightened by war but cannot opt out.

13. The first person is used to draw the reader in to the text.
14. Friendly
15. 7: mules, horses, elephants, camels, dogs, pigeons, cats

16–17. 'Crashed' means the plane went down unavoidably, 'ditched' means the plane made a forced landing on water/the sea.

18. Only stray dogs were used to carry messages in the First World War.
19. 24 November 2004
20. The actions of animals can save people's lives.

**Answers to 21–26 might include:**

21. The cold pinched our cheeks with frost-fringed <u>fingers</u>.
22. The shop was crowded with people buying boxes of <u>balloons</u>.
23. My Gran's peach pies are <u>perfect</u>.
24. The bird soared over the tops of the tallest <u>trees</u>.
25. I tried to reach the bargain bucket while people <u>pushed</u> passed me.
26. The children sat <u>silently</u> in school.

27–31. furthermore, moreover

nevertheless, however

therefore, consequently

because, as

in contrast, on the other hand

32. margarine
33. benefit
34. grammar
35. syllable
36. parliament
37. emphasis
38. journalist
39. signature
40. tension
41. confusion
42. magician
43. politician
44. attention
45. direction
46. electrician
47. explosion
48. fiction
49. formal
50. informal
51. formal
52. informal
53. formal
54. formal
55. 'Everybody will have to pay tax...' the Chancellor began.
56. I won the 100 metres race at school today<u>;</u> afterwards, we went out for a pizza!

57–58. There was a huge selection in the new bakers: the chocolate choux buns filled with cream<u>;</u> the cinnamon rolls with juicy raisins and the hot mince pies were my favourites.

**Answers to 59–62 might include:**

59. a bouncy, blue balloon
60. a scary, silver spider
61. an extremely hard test
62. a delicious chocolate ice-cream

**Answers to 63–70 might include:**

63–64. preposition, adjective
65–66. verb, noun
67–68. adverb, pronoun
69–70. definite article, indefinite article

## PAPER 10

1. Hind Street
2. two weeks
3. blue
4. The shop would have been opened earlier and all the jewellery would have been taken out of the safe, not just the watches and chains.
5. They alerted all their patrols.
6. Someone who is involved in a crime with someone else.
7. Answers might include: Lizzy Butler would have felt very frightened during the robbery because the men were armed and might have hurt her.
8. It had distinctive italicised number plates.

9–10. It might still be somewhere in the town, or it could have left the town along the B154 Bisham Road.

11. They think they might try to sell it.
12. By offering a community award.
13. Raining/wet (The jeweller is late because of the flooding and the robbers left wet footprints.)

14. Rhyming is used in the heading: 'Double Trouble'.

15–16. By telephone on 01791 761004 or email on jsquare@peaseburystation.org

17. 3: the two robbers in the shop and a getaway driver

18. Mr Marley is Lizzy Butler's uncle. The text states that she is his niece in paragraph 6 ('niece' is not an acceptable answer because the question asks how Mr Marley is related to Lizzy).

19. 2, 5, 6

20. gold-plated analogue watches with expandable straps; 16-, 18- and 20-inch gold rope chains, stamped with London hallmark

21. I finished my homework while my brother watched TV.

22. I enjoy gymnastics; however, Paul prefers hockey.

23. It was funny when the clown threw the custard pie.

24. I have to use my old bag until I can afford a new one.

25. The hotel had a great swimming pool so we spent a lot of time there.

26. My brother is younger than me, although he is taller.

27. the children's toys

28. the three boys' houses

29. a witch's hat

30. the people's bags

31. the men's newspapers

32. the trees' trunks

33. Petra followed the ghostly figure around the churchyard.

34. Jacob won't be back until teatime.

35. Claire told the secret to her friend.

36. Dad mended the broken vase with strong glue.

37. Rebecca spent all of her pocket money on sweets.

38. Eating lots of fruit and vegetables is very good for you.

39. My brother is really accomplished at climbing over fences.

40. The party starts at 4.30pm.

41. Jane and Savion (a pain-in-the-neck from Class 4) were asked to work the computer in assembly.

42. Flix and Flax (yapping toy poodles) won the best-dressed dogs' rosette.

43. My brothers (spotty with annoying habits) always shut me out of their bedroom.

44. Morebridge Rovers (the awful local team) are playing at the rec on Sunday after lunch.

45. The Year 6 class at Rowtree Primary were trying to win the prize for best-behaved class (no chance there then!)

46. Swimming in the shallow end (well paddling) was Ethel's favourite pastime.

47–52. megabyte, text message, memory stick, wind farm, carbon footprint

**Answers to 53–60 might include:**

53. dough

54. plead

55. sour

56. treat

57. tried

58. fire

59. heard

60. stable

61. simile

62. simile

63. metaphor

64. metaphor

65. Oliver ate the crunchy apple

66. The girls read their books quietly.

67. I don't like arguments

68. The team won their match

69. We have a new car

70. It was time to go and Amy could not find her shoes

10 The boys were starting to feel the chill now, in their damp clothes. They had eaten their packed lunches almost as soon as the coach left school and now they felt hungry. To make matters worse the floors of the tunnels, which were just damp when they had set off, were now submerged under a thin layer of water, which was getting deeper all the time.

11 With a jolt of relief, Tom had an idea. He got out his mobile phone. 'We'll just ring for help,' he said, grinning. But of course, so far underground, there was no signal.

12 'We'll have to split up to look for a way out,' said James, desperately.

### Underline your answers.

**1.** What sort of group made the trip in the story?

a family        a youth group        a school class        a group of boys

**2.** Where did the guide deliver 'the briefing?'

in a tunnel        at the cave mouth        in the coach        inside the caves

**3.** How many boys get lost in the cave system?

the whole class        two        three        four

/3

### Answer these questions.

**4.** Find and copy a word from the text that describes a type of rain. _____

**5.** What did Tom's mother say that might have made him take the guide's warnings less seriously?

_____

**6.** How does the weather above the ground affect the risks the boys face in the caves?

_____

**7.** One of the passages the boys come across is 'well lit'. Why does Tom assume that the group won't have gone along it?

_____

**8.** How can the boys still see where they are going in the passages without electric lights?

_____

**9–10.** Apart from fear, find two ways in which the boys feel uncomfortable after they get lost.

_____   _____

**11.** Apart from the clothes they were wearing, the boys only have torches and a mobile phone. Write a sentence to explain which would be more useful to them and why.

_____

_____

**12.** Do you think it would be a good idea for the boys to split up to find a way out? Write a sentence to explain why.

_____

_____

**13.** List the different sorts of lights mentioned in the text.

_____

_____

**14.** Underline the pair of words from **paragraph** 5 that suggest the boys have begun to panic.

| | |
|---|---|
| silence | tunnels |
| narrow | slippery |
| skidding | raced |
| turn | pass |

**15.** Think of a suitable title for this story.

_____

**16.** Find a **simile** in the text._____

**17.** At the end of which paragraph would this sentence best fit? Underline the correct paragraph number.

_She had been busy packing their lunches and shook her head as she read the health and safety warning on the form he had brought home._

paragraph 2     paragraph 4     paragraph 6     paragraph 10

**18.** Underline the statement which best sums up the moral of the story.

Always take your mobile phone.

Always take a torch.

Listen to your Mum.

Listen to safety instructions.

**19.** Underline the most appropriate description of the story's ending.

a resolution

a conflict

a cliffhanger

a moral

**20.** Find four pieces of evidence in the text that show it was written in the 20th or 21st century.

_____    _____

_____    _____    /17

Write these sentences again with **passive verbs**.

**21.** The cat scratched the little girl.

_____

**22.** An owl's hoot shattered the silence.

_____

**23.** Tara wrote the best story.

_____

**24.** Mum built a rockery in the garden.

_____

**25.** Roadworks held up the traffic.

_____

**26.** The rain stopped the cricket match.

_____    /6

Write the **plurals** of these words.

**27.** butterfly _____    **28.** child _____

**29.** goose _____    **30.** man _____

**31.** sheep _____    **32.** tooth _____    /6

Write this piece of text again adding punctuation, including speech marks. Remember to start a new line each time a different person speaks.

**33–48.** Are we nearly there whined Oscar Not too much further replied Dad Can we go straight to the beach when we get there begged Oscar If you like laughed Dad

_____

_____

_____

_____    /16

Write an **antonym** for each of the underlined words.

**49.** Anna was <u>sorry</u> that the holidays were over.    _____

**50.** <u>Fortunately</u>, a new road is being built to carry the extra traffic.    _____

**51.** Dad is <u>buying</u> a car.    _____

**52.** I am the <u>tallest</u> in my class.    _____

**53.** The train to Birmingham is due to <u>arrive</u> at 3.15.    _____

**54.** The maths homework was quite <u>difficult</u>.    _____    /6

Choose whether each sentence is a **metaphor** or **simile**.

**55.** The crystal dewdrops hung on the spider's web. _____

**56.** The boys scurried through the tunnels like ants. _____

**57.** The engine purred like a panther as he raced
down the country lanes. _____

**58.** The tight fist of anger gripped his heart. _____

**59.** His razor-sharp vision spotted the culprit. _____

**60.** Lemonade as sparkling as champagne
was served at lunch. _____

/6

Rewrite these sentences, correcting the errors.

**61–62.** The twins wore diffrent outfits too the fancy dress party.

_____

_____

**63–64.** When the performance ended, several acters went shoping for replacement costumes.

_____

_____ /4

Rewrite these sentences, beginning with the underlined word.

**65.** James found a new place to hide his secret letter <u>under</u> the tree.

_____

_____

**66.** There was an old World War Two pillbox <u>behind</u> the bike sheds.

_____

_____

**67.** When she fell over the tree trunk, <u>Gemma</u> broke her arm.

_____

_____

**68.** Their new poodle Daisy's favourite pastimes were <u>jumping</u> and bouncing.

_____

_____

**69.** The estuary was covered with <u>thick</u> fog.

_____

**70.** The '70s outfit was <u>sadly</u> too small for Kishori.

_____   /6

/70

## PAPER 7

1   If there was one thing we loved in 6C, it was having a supply teacher. There was something delicious about ruining their lessons a bit at a time. The disappointing ones (like Mr Wilkins who came in last Tuesday) crumbled by morning break and, after a stiff talking-to from the head teacher Mr Singh, we'd be doing colouring-in and handwriting practice in silence for the rest of the day. The best ones had a bit of fight in them, providing us with entertainment until lunchtime at least. Either way we would always end up doing handwriting and colouring.

2   This one, in particular, looked like she was going to be a pushover. Neat and tidy Miss Smith, our usual class teacher, had conquered us over the autumn and spring terms with a combination of zero tolerance of mischief-making and ruthless efficiency. Her lessons were planned with military precision. Handouts for the entire week were colour coded and laid out in regiments on her desk. Completed the work early? No problem, try pink worksheet 3.2. Work too easy? Green 2.8. Too hard? Beige 1.2. Whatever your excuse for not working, Miss Smith could put her hand on the solution in a heartbeat.

3   The same could not be said of today's supply teacher, Miss Mess. Across the desk, and most other horizontal surfaces in the room, were higgledy-piggledy piles of Miss Smith's precious worksheets stacked, it appeared, in random order.

4   We took one look at the chaos and smiled. With Miss Smith's worksheet system out of action, Miss Mess would have to rely on a zero-tolerance policy on behaviour. In her tent dress and comfy shoes, she really didn't look the type to pull it off.

5   'Good morning, 6C,' said Miss Mess in a small, feeble voice. 'Please sit down.' The class remained standing, waiting to see what she would do next. We were in for a surprise.

6   'I said, sit down 6C,' said Miss Mess, more forcefully, fixing the class with a curious, powerful stare.

7   The better-mannered children in 6C took their seats. The rest of us began to experience a strange sensation behind the knees. It began with a tingle that became numbness and then a distinct weakness. Several of us had the good sense to sit down before our legs collapsed beneath them. A few continued in their defiance and ended up wriggling on the floor like slugs.

8   Miss Mess, it seemed, would be no pushover.

### Underline your answers.

**1.** What was the name of Class 6C's usual teacher?

Mr Singh        Miss Smith      Mr Wilkins        Miss Mess

**2.** How long had she been teaching the class?

two months      spring term      two terms        two years

**3.** Which method did Miss Smith not use to teach Class 6C?

zero tolerance of mischief-making

ruthless efficiency

precision-planned lessons

colouring-in and handwriting practice

/3

### Answer these questions.

**4.** What did 6C like best about having a supply teacher?

_____

**5.** What does the word 'delicious' (**paragraph** 1, line 2) tell us about how the children feel when they tease the supply teacher?

_____

**6–7.** What two things happened to the class if they didn't obey Miss Mess?

_____

_____

**8–9.** Find two war-type phrases which suggest that Miss Smith has had to battle with 6C.

_____

_____

**10.** Why might the contrast in how the teachers look affect how the children behave for Miss Mess?

_____

_____

**11.** What does the word 'horizontal' (paragraph 3) mean?

_____

**12.** Do you think Miss Mess is like the other supply teachers the children have had? Explain your answer.

_____

_____

**13.** What would happen if you completed your work early?

_____

**14.** What does the word 'pushover' mean in the final line of the text?

_____

**15.** Into which paragraph would this new sentence best fit? Underline the paragraph number.

*She hadn't even managed to button up her cardigan in the correct holes, so there was no chance of surviving 6C!*

paragraph 2     paragraph 4     paragraph 5     paragraph 7

**16.** What **tense** is this text written in? _____

**17.** Why does the writer use the phrase 'in a heartbeat' (**paragraph** 2)?

_____

**18.** Underline the pair of words that best reflect the writer's view of Miss Smith.

entertaining     stiff

disorganised    quiet

strong          effective

disappointing   pushover

**19.** Underline the genre this text could fit into.

instructional    fantasy         myth            historical

**20.** Tick the true statement.

All the children in 6C took their seats when Miss Mess told them.

Miss Mess was a pushover.

Miss Smith was a supply teacher.

A few children wriggled on the floor like slugs.

/17

Add *did* or *done* to complete each sentence.

**21.** I _____ my homework before I watched TV.

**22.** When the window was broken, the girls admitted they had _____ it.

**23–24.** I _____ not do the washing up because I thought my sister had _____ it.

**25–26.** When I saw the picture that Chris had _____, I _____ one just like it.

/6

Write this passage again, adding the capital letters and punctuation.

**27–41.** *settle down class said the teacher she gave each of us a question paper an answer paper and a sharp pencil the teacher said you have 30 minutes for the test and the time starts now*

_____

_____

_____ **/15**

Write these sentences again, changing the **nouns** and **verbs** to their **plural** form.

**42.** Our cat sleeps on my bed.

_____

**43.** My friend is eating an orange.

_____

**44.** The road was very busy.

_____

**45.** My brother is playing a computer game.

_____

**46.** The teacher collects my book.

_____ **/5**

Add a **prefix** or **suffix** to each **root word** to make a new word. Remember to make any necessary changes to spelling.

**47.** partner _____  **48.** usual _____

**49.** music _____  **50.** comfort _____

**51.** free _____  **52.** decorate _____  **/8**

**53.** fortune _____  **54.** curious _____

Choose a word from the list to match each of these word types.

they   massive   dance   Paris   silently   notebook

**55.** verb _____   **56.** noun _____

**57.** pronoun _____   **58.** proper noun _____

**59.** adjective _____   **60.** adverb _____   /6

Add **colons** and **semi-colons** to complete each sentence.

**61.** We brought Freddie a season ticket for his birthday_____ he loved rugby.

**62.** Jennel bought her ingredients from the supermarket_____ chocolate drops, flour, margarine, milk and silver balls.

**63.** Denny_____ Where did I leave my glasses? (exit, stage left)

**64–66.** Under her bed, Maddie found_____ a mouldy apple, half eaten_____ a packet of

peppermint chewing gum_____ two sugar mice with fluff all over them.   /6

Rewrite these sentences, correcting the errors.

**67–68.** The rapping paper was covered with baloons and ribbons.

_____

_____

**69–70.** The cake's iceing was turquoise and pink with grate big decorative plastic flowers.

_____

_____   /4

/70

### Theseus and the Minotaur

1 Long ago, a feud raged between King Minos of Crete and King Aegeus of Athens. The son of Minos had been attacked and killed in Athens and, despite his best efforts, Aegeus had been unable to find the culprits. Eventually, Aegeus had to agree to hand over seven young men and seven young women to Minos every seven years. These people were taken to Crete where they were fed to the Minotaur, a fearsome beast which was imprisoned in a labyrinth beneath the palace.

2 The son of Aegeus, who was called Theseus, was unhappy with the deal that had been struck. He begged his father to allow him to be one of the seven young men sent to Crete and promised that once there he would kill the Minotaur. Aegeus reluctantly agreed, and Theseus prepared to set sail for Crete, with the thirteen other young men and women who were to enter the labyrinth. He told his father that, if he was successful, he would use a white sail on the return voyage, so that Athens would know of his victory all the sooner.

3 When the boat arrived at Crete, King Minos was waiting for them with his daughter Ariadne, who took one look at Theseus and fell in love with him. Later that night, she crept to the cell he was being held in. Giving him a ball of thread, she told him to tie it to the door of the labyrinth and let it unravel as he moved through the passages, so that he would be able to find his way back to the entrance. She also gave him a powerful sword with which to slay the Minotaur. In return, she made him promise to take her with him when he left Crete.

4 The next morning, the young Athenians were taken to the labyrinth and shut inside. Leaving the others at the entrance, Theseus tied the thread to the door and went alone into the maze of passages. Some time later he heard the Minotaur moving in the darkness ahead of him. He rounded a corner and there it was, huge and powerful, with the body of a man and the head of a bull, bellowing and snorting ferociously. Theseus and the Minotaur fought furiously but eventually Theseus managed to slay the beast and find his way back out of the labyrinth.

5 True to his word, Theseus took Ariadne with him when he left Crete, but he soon tired of his saviour and decided not to take her with him back to Greece. Having refilled the boat's supply of fresh water on the island of Naxos, Theseus left Ariadne asleep and set sail for home. This angered the gods, who punished Theseus by making him forget to use a white sail on the voyage back to Athens. Seeing a black sail, Aegeus assumed that Theseus had been killed by the Minotaur and in his grief he threw himself into the sea and died. Theseus became king, but never forgave himself for causing his father's death.

**Underline your answers.**

**1.** Who was the father of Theseus?

King Midas     King Minos     King Aegeus     the Minotaur

**2.** How many young people travelled to Crete?

7          10          13          14

**3.** Where did Theseus leave Ariadne?

Athens     Naxos     Greece     Crete

/3

**Answer these questions.**

**4.** What is the meaning of the word 'feud' (**paragraph** 1)?

_____

**5.** Do you think Aegeus was confident that Theseus would kill the Minotaur?
Give a reason for your answer.

_____

_____

**6.** How did Theseus plan to get news of his safety to his father as quickly as possible?

_____

_____

**7.** What is a labyrinth? _____

**8.** Why would a labyrinth be a good place to imprison a beast as terrible as the Minotaur?

_____

_____

**9.** Explain how the ball of thread helped Theseus in the labyrinth.

_____

_____

**10.** Do you think Theseus would have been able to slay the Minotaur without Ariadne's help? Use evidence from the text to back up your answer.

_____

_____

**11.** Why were the gods angry when Theseus left Ariadne on the island?

_____

**12.** What was the effect of the god's punishment on Aegeus?

_____

_____

**13.** Underline the word closest in meaning to 'culprits' (**paragraph** 1).

young men       beasts          sailors            murderers

**14.** Tick the thing that Theseus did not do.

Sail to Minos.                    Use a white sail.

Kill the Minotaur.               Become King of Athens.

**15.** Which three paragraphs begin with time **connectives**?

_____

**16.** Choose the correct order for these events in 'Theseus and the Minotaur'.

**a**     What happened in the labyrinth.

**b**     King Aegeus agrees to send young people to Minos.

**c**     The events of Theseus' return journey.

**d**     Theseus is unhappy about the agreement between the King of Crete and the King of Athens.

**a, d, c, b**        **b, d, a, c**        **a, b, c, d**            **b, a, c, d**

**17.** Underline how you think Ariadne felt when she was left on the island.

apathetic          distraught        ecstatic           contented

**18.** Underline the two things that Aegeus saw when Theseus returned to Athens.

white sail          black sail          ship               Theseus

**19.** What phrase in the first paragraph suggests that this narrative is a myth?

_____

**20.** Find an example of **onomatopoeia** in **paragraph** 4.

_____ /17

Write these words again, adding the missing silent letter.

**21.** coco _____

**22.** gost _____

**23.** ryme _____

**24.** lepard _____

**25.** anser _____

**26.** naw _____

**27.** lam _____

**28.** gitar _____

/8

Write this passage again, separating the words and adding capital letters and punctuation.

**29–43.** _wecreptthroughtheforestlookingcarefullyaboutuslooktheresonesaiddadwelookedupand sawaredsquirrelinthebranchesaboveusitlookedatusforamomentthenleaptintoanothertree_

_____

_____

_____

_____ /15

Write these words again, as statements.

**44.** Is the theatre near here?

_____

**45.** Do I have to be back before it gets dark?

_____

**46.** Will we have enough time to finish our work?

_____

**47.** Can we have fish and chips for tea?

/4

_____

Write a **homophone** for each word, then write a short **definition** for both words.

**48–50.** find

_____   _____

_____   _____

**51–53.** real

_____   _____

_____   _____

**54–56.** hair

_____   _____

_____   _____  **/9**

Find a **synonym** for each of the underlined words.

**57.** 'Are you going to drama club tonight?' <u>said</u> Beth.   _____

**58.** The motorcyclists in the display team were <u>amazing</u>!   _____

**59.** Creeping <u>silently</u>, the fox hunted the rabbit.   _____

**60.** The <u>thick</u> fog was impossible to see through.   _____

**61.** 'That's not yours, it's mine,' <u>cried</u> Mandy.   _____

**62.** The <u>wizened</u> old man peered through the keyhole.   _____  **/6**

Write down two words that start with each **prefix**.

**63–64.** with   _____   _____

**65–66.** fore   _____   _____

**67–68.** inter   _____   _____

**69–70.** under   _____   _____  **/8**

**/70**

## PAPER 9

1   When we think about the First and Second World Wars, we tend to think about the people who were fighting, or what it was like for those left behind at home. Behind the scenes, however, hundreds of thousands of animals risked their lives to support the war effort, showing such bravery that many were later awarded medals.

2   Around 16 million animals served in the First World War (1914–1918), including mules, horses, elephants and camels. Many were used to transport troops and equipment across a variety of difficult terrains. Dogs were also used to carry messages from trench to trench when telephone wires were damaged by shellfire. They wore metal canisters attached to their collars to store the messages and were able to cover rough, broken ground much more quickly than a man could. Initially only stray dogs were used, but as the war dragged on, more than 7,000 people offered their pet dogs for training.

3   During the Second World War (1939–1945), dogs were even trained as paradogs, being parachuted with their handlers into enemy territory, where they helped to track and attack the enemy and sniff out mines and other hidden explosives. One dog, Rob, made 22 parachute drops. Dogs were also used both in Britain and behind enemy lines to search for the wounded after bombing raids.

4   Elephants were used to help build bridges and to move aircraft and other heavy machinery in the Far East. They were perfect for the job, being both very strong and able to reach remote parts of the jungle in Burma that no vehicle could.

5   Pigeons were used to carry messages in both World Wars with around half a million birds being used. Although communications technology had improved by the Second World War, pigeons were often the only reliable way to get messages behind enemy lines.

6   As well as carrying messages, the birds were routinely carried by RAF aircrews during the Second World War, so that if the plane crashed or ditched in the sea, the birds could fly back to Britain carrying details of the crew's location. Around 20,000 pigeons died while carrying out their duties and pigeons received more medals for bravery than any other species. They were such effective messengers that the Swiss army continued to use them until 50 years after the end of the Second World War.

7   The medal awarded to animals is the Dickin Medal, also known as the Animals' Victoria Cross. The medal was named after Maria Dickin, who founded the animal charity PDSA. Between 1943 and 1949, medals were awarded to animals who

displayed outstanding bravery. This included 32 pigeons, 18 dogs, three horses and a cat.

8   A monument unveiled in London on 24 November 2004 is dedicated to the bravery of animals in war. The script reads as follows: 'To all the animals that served and died alongside British and Allied forces in wars and campaigns throughout time. They had no choice.'

**Underline your answers.**

1. Where were elephants used during World War Two?

England      India      Burma      Africa

2. When did the Swiss army stop using pigeons to carry messages?

1943      1945      1968      1995

3. How many Dickin Medals, mentioned in the text, were awarded between 1943 and 1949.

18      32      45      54

/3

**Answer these questions.**

4. Why might animals like mules and camels sometimes be better at transporting troops and equipment than trucks?

_____

_____

5. Why do you think people offered their pet dogs for use in the trenches?

_____

6–7. Find two jobs that dogs did during the Second World War.

_____

_____

8. Why were elephants so useful in the jungle?

_____

**9.** Why were pigeons still used to carry messages during the Second World War, despite improvements in communications technology?

_____

_____

**10.** What was the benefit for RAF crews carrying pigeons?

_____

_____

**11–12.** The script on the monument in London says that animals that die in wars have 'no choice'. Is it fair to use animals in this way? Write one argument in favour of using animals like this and one argument against.

for: _____

_____

against: _____

_____

**13.** Why is the first **paragraph** written in the first person and the rest of the text in the third person?

_____

**14.** Underline the word closest in meaning to 'Allied' (paragraph 8).

　　Alley　　　　　　Enemy　　　　　　Friendly　　　　　French

**15.** How many different species of animals are mentioned in the text? Underline the correct number.

　　3　　　　　　　5　　　　　　　7　　　　　　　9

**16–17.** What is the difference between 'crashed' and 'ditched' in paragraph 6?

_____

_____

**18.** Tick the statement that is not true.

There is a monument in London dedicated to brave animals.

Only one cat received a medal for bravery in the Second World War.

Only stray dogs were used to carry messages in the First World War.

The Swiss army used pigeons in 1990.

**19.** What is the earliest date this article could have been written?

_____

**20.** Tick the quote that is most likely to have been written by the author of this article.

The actions of animals can save people's lives.

Pigeons are vermin.

Bravery isn't a word you can use about animals.

People would be better off without pets.

/17

**Complete each sentence with a suitable alliterative word.**

**21.** The cold pinched our cheeks with frost-fringed _____.

**22.** The shop was crowded with people buying boxes of _____.

**23.** My Gran's peach pies are _____.

**24.** The bird soared over the tops of the tallest _____.

**25.** I tried to reach the bargain bucket while people _____ past me.

**26.** The children sat _____ in school.

/6

**Draw lines to join up the pairs of connectives with similar meanings.**

**27–31.**
| | |
|---|---|
| furthermore | on the other hand |
| nevertheless | as |
| therefore | however |
| because | moreover |
| in contrast | consequently |

/5

Add the missing unstressed vowel to each word.

**32.** marg_____rine

**33.** ben_____fit

**34.** gramm_____r

**35.** syll_____ble

**36.** parli_____ment

**37.** emph_____sis

**38.** journ_____list

**39.** sign_____ture

/8

Add the **suffix** *cian*, *sion* or *tion* to complete each word.

**40.** ten_____

**41.** confu_____

**42.** magi_____

**43.** politi_____

**44.** atten_____

**45.** direc_____

**46.** electri_____

**47.** explo_____

**48.** fic_____

/9

Put a tick by each sentence that uses formal language
and a cross by those that do not.

**49.** Children are not permitted on school property between the hours of 4.30pm and 8.45am.

**50.** Let's go bowling after school.

**51.** Your bank account has been credited with the agreed funds.

**52.** Thanks for the great present!

**53.** Parking is prohibited.

**54.** A valid licence and permit must be held in order to fish in this river.

/6

Add **colons**, **semi-colons** or **ellipses** to complete each sentence.

**55.** 'Everybody will have to pay tax_____ the Chancellor began.

**56.** I won the 100 metres race at school today_____ afterwards, we went out for a pizza!

**57–58.** There was a huge selection in the new bakers_____ the chocolate choux buns filled

with cream_____ the cinnamon rolls with juicy raisins and the hot mince pies

were my favourites.                                                                    /4

---

Write an **adjectival phrase** to describe each thing.

**59.** a balloon        _____

**60.** a spider         _____

**61.** a test           _____

**62.** ice-cream        _____        /4

---

Identify the word types of the underlined words.
Choose from the list below.

---

noun   adjective   verb   adverb   pronoun   preposition   definite article   indefinite article

---

**63–64.** High in the rainforest trees, pools of water provide homes for frogs.

_____    _____

**65–66.** Professor Jarmain researches species of bat that frequent the forest canopy.

_____    _____

**67–68.** Blue morpho butterflies flit gracefully from flower to flower as they collect nectar.

_____    _____

**69–70.** The three-toed sloth hung lethargically from a mahogany tree.

_____    _____        /8

/70

### Local Jeweller in Double Trouble

1. Police are appealing for witnesses to come forward after a town centre jeweller was robbed for the second time in a fortnight. Marley's Jeweller was targeted on Thursday as staff arrived for work in the morning. Thieves stole watches and gold chains to the value of around £13,000 from the Hind Street store, but store manager Gerald Marley says that it could have been much worse.

2. 'We were late opening the shop that day because I got held up by the flooding on the Peasebury bypass. Normally by that time all the jewellery would have been taken out of the safe. As it was, we had only had time to get out the watches and some of the gold chains.'

3. Two men, who are believed to have been armed, burst into the shop at 9.45 on Thursday morning as Mr Marley and shop assistant Lizzy Butler were arranging the displays of watches and chains. The robbers' faces were partially covered but they were both white with brown hair. One was tall with a slim build, the other short and stockily built. The taller man threatened Miss Butler while his accomplice grabbed handfuls of jewellery and stuffed it into the pockets of a black leather jacket.

4. Police believe there was a further man waiting in a getaway car behind the shop in Bridge Street. The car, an estate with distinctive italicised number plates, was spotted speeding off down Hind Street, but what happened to it after that remains a mystery.

5. Chief Inspector Rob Day explains, 'Mr Marley raised the alarm as soon as the thieves had left the store and we immediately alerted all of our patrols to be on the lookout for the car. If the thieves had made their escape along the bypass, they would have been seen by one of the police patrols who were controlling the queues of traffic. It seems most likely that if they left the town at all, it would have been via the B154 Bisham Road. However, we are not ruling out the possibility that the thieves live in the town, especially since they were, we believe, the same men involved in another robbery at the store on the 12th August, from the shape of the wet footprints left on both occasions.'

6. 'This was obviously a very serious attack and although fortunately nobody was hurt, both Mr Marley and his niece, Ms Butler, are clearly very shaken up. We are very keen to catch these men before they have the chance to strike again.'

7   Anyone who saw a navy-coloured estate car in the Hind Street area of the town on Thursday morning, or has seen it since, is asked to contact the police station on 01791 761004. Similarly, the police are asking for people to get in touch if they are offered watches or gold chains to buy under suspicious circumstances. There is a community award for information leading to the conviction of the thieves.

*Incident officer: Sgt Janice Square jsquare@peaseburystation.org*

## Underline your answers.

**1.** On what street is Marley's Jeweller?

   Bridge Street    Hind Street    Bisham Road    Peasebury

**2.** How far apart were the two robberies?

   one week        two weeks        three weeks        four weeks

**3.** What colour was the getaway car?

   black            blue            silver            green

/3

## Answer these questions.

**4.** Why would the robbery have been worse if it had taken place on any other day?

_____

_____

**5.** What was the first action the police took after the second robbery?

_____

**6.** What is the meaning of the word 'accomplice' (**paragraph** 3)?

_____

**7.** Write a sentence describing how you think Lizzy Butler would have felt during the robbery.

_____

_____

**8.** What was unusual about the appearance of the car that witnesses may have noticed?

_____

**9–10.** What two things do the police think might have happened to the car after it was seen speeding away down Hind Street?

_____

_____

**11.** What do the police think the thieves might try to do with the stolen jewellery?

_____

**12.** How do the police hope to encourage people to come forward with information?

_____

**13.** What was the weather like on the day of the robbery?

_____

**14.** Find an example of rhyming used for effect in the text.

_____

**15–16.** Find two ways that you could contact the police about the robbery.

_____

_____

**17.** How many people do the police believe were involved in the second robbery? _____

**18.** How is Mr Marley related to Lizzy Butler?

_____

**19.** Which **paragraphs** include quotations? Underline the correct answer.

　　　1, 2, 3　　　　　2, 4, 6　　　　　2, 6, 7　　　　　2, 5, 6

**20.** Tick the two descriptions that would most likely be distributed by the police.

　　　delightful watches with pretty straps

　　　gold-plated analogue watches with expandable straps

　　　16-, 18- and 20-inch solid gold rope chains, stamped with London hallmark

　　　really expensive chunky chains

/17

Add a suitable **conjunction** from the list to complete each sentence. You can only use each conjunction once.

**until   when   while   so   however   although**

**21.** I finished my homework _____ my brother watched TV.

**22.** I enjoy gymnastics; _____, Paul prefers hockey.

**23.** It was funny _____ the clown threw the custard pie.

**24.** I have to use my old bag _____ I can afford a new one.

**25.** The hotel had a great swimming pool _____ we spent a lot of time there.

**26.** My brother is younger than me, _____ he is taller.

/6

Circle the correct use of the **apostrophe** in each pair of phrases.

**27.** the children's toys          the childrens' toys

**28.** the three boy's houses      the three boys' houses

**29.** a witch's hat                a witches' hat

**30.** the peoples' bags           the people's bags

**31.** the mens' newspapers        the men's newspapers

**32.** the trees' trunks           the tree's trunks

/6

Add a suitable **preposition** from the list to complete each sentence. You can only use each preposition once.

**to   with   around   for   over   until   at   on**

**33.** Petra followed the ghostly figure _____ the churchyard.

**34.** Jacob won't be back _____ teatime.

**35.** Claire told the secret _____ her friend.

**36.** Dad mended the broken vase _____ strong glue.

**37.** Rebecca spent all of her pocket money _____ sweets.

**38.** Eating lots of fruit and vegetables is very good _____ you.

**39.** My brother is really accomplished at climbing _____ fences.

**40.** The party starts _____ 4.30pm.

> Rewrite these sentences, inserting brackets where necessary.

**41.** Jane and Savion a pain-in-the-neck from Class 4 were asked to work the computer in assembly.

_____

_____

**42.** Flix and Flax yapping toy poodles won the best-dressed dogs' rosette.

_____

_____

**43.** My brothers spotty with annoying habits always shut me out of their bedroom.

_____

_____

**44.** Morebridge Rovers the awful local team are playing at the rec on Sunday after lunch.

_____

_____

**45.** The Year 6 class at Rowtree Primary were trying to win the prize for best-behaved class no chance there then!

_____

_____

**46.** Swimming in the shallow end well paddling was Ethel's favourite pastime.

_____

_____

/6

Underline the words and phrases that have entered the English language in the past 100 years.

**47–52.** megabyte      text message      field      pan

memory stick      plough      iron      castle

wind farm      windmill      journal      carbon footprint

**/6**

Write down a word with the same underlined letter string as each word, but a different pronunciation.

**53.** c<u>ough</u> _____    **54.** br<u>ea</u>d _____

**55.** hon<u>our</u> _____    **56.** sw<u>ea</u>t _____

**57.** p<u>ie</u>ce _____    **58.** shir<u>t</u> _____

**59.** f<u>ear</u> _____    **60.** port<u>able</u> _____

**/8**

Write '**simile**' or '**metaphor**' beside each phrase.

**61.** He is as gentle as a lamb. _____

**62.** She had hair like spun gold. _____

**63.** My cousins are little devils. _____

**64.** The moon was a pale balloon in the sky. _____

**/4**

Underline the **subject** and circle the **object** of each sentence.

**65.** Oliver ate the crunchy apple.

**66.** The girls read their books quietly.

**67.** I don't like arguments.

**68.** The team won their match.

**69.** We have a new car.

**70.** It was time to go and Amy could not find her shoes.

**/6**

**/70**

| | |
|---|---|
| **active verb** | a **verb** where the **subject** of the sentence is the main focus, e.g *The man ate the apple.* |
| **adjectival phrase** | a group of words that describe a **noun**, e.g. *the beautiful, tiny bird* |
| **adjective** | a word that describes a **noun**, e.g. *tiny, green* |
| **adverb** | a word that describes a **verb**, e.g. *kindly, prettily* |
| **alliteration** | creative writing technique where two or more words in a sentence begin with the same sound, e.g. *slimy slugs* |
| **antonym** | a word with the opposite meaning to another word, e.g. *tall, short* |
| **apostrophe** | a punctuation mark (') used to show possession or **contraction** |
| **assonance** | the similarity or repetition of two or more vowel sounds, especially in words that are close together in a poem, e.g. *The wind sings in the valley.* |
| **clause** | a part of a sentence that contains a **verb** |
| **colon** | a punctuation mark (:) used to introduce a list, quotation or a second **clause** which adds information to the first, e.g. *For our picnic we bought: French bread, cheese, strawberries and bananas.* |
| **complex sentence** | a sentence that contains a **main clause** and one or more **subordinate clauses**. |
| **conditional clause** | a **clause** in a sentence which describes how one thing depends on another, e.g. *If it is cold, I will wear a hat.* |
| **conjunction** | a word used to join parts of a sentence, e.g. *and, but, so* |
| **connective** | a word or words that join **clauses** or sentences, e.g. *They played together until it was time to go home.* |
| **contraction** | two words joined together, where an **apostrophe** marks letters that have been removed, e.g. *do not = don't* |
| **definite article** | a word (in English the word 'the') that goes together with a **noun** to refer to a specific object, place, animal or person e.g. *the saucepan, the garden, the giraffes, the boy* |
| **definition** | the meaning of a word |
| **direct speech** | what someone says, using their actual words, e.g. *'Give it to me!'* |
| **ellipsis** | a punctuation (…) mark that shows something has been missed out, to show the passage of time, or thoughts, e.g. *The Prime Minister thought how he could win more votes… he would give everybody an extra holiday!* |

**homophone**      a word which sounds the same but which has a different spelling, e.g. *maid, made*

**indefinite article**      a word (in English 'a' or 'an') that goes together with a **noun** to refer to a general object, place, animal or person, e.g. *a saucepan, a garden, a giraffe, a boy, an orange*

**indirect speech**      what someone has said, without their actual words being used, e.g. *Jake complained about his sister again.*

**main clause**      a **clause** which could stand alone as a sentence, e.g. *There are no poisonous spiders in Britain, but many British people are scared of spiders.*

**metaphor**      where one thing is described as being another, e.g. *He is a star.*

**noun**      a word or group of words used as the name of a class of people, places or things, e.g. *players, playground, balls*, or for a specific person, point in time, place or thing (see **proper noun**)

**object**      the person or thing that the **verb** relates to in a sentence, e.g. *Lisa sang a song.*

**onomatopoeia**      a word that makes the sound that it describes, e.g. *bang*

**paragraph**      a section of a piece of writing, used to organise information: a new paragraph indicates a change in topic, place, time or speaker

**passive verb**      a **verb** where the **object** of the sentence is the focus, e.g. *The nut was eaten by the squirrel.*

**personification**      where non-human things are described as having human qualities, e.g. *The Sun smiled on us.*

**plural**      more than one of something, e.g. *cars, children*

**prefix**      a group of letters added to the beginning of a word to alter its meaning, e.g. *re, ex, co*

**preposition**      a word that describes the position of one thing in relation to another, e.g. *on, under, from*

**pronoun**      a word that can be used in the place of a **noun**, e.g. *he, she, they*

**proper noun**      the name of a person, place, day of the week, month of the year, e.g. *Jill, Rome, Tuesday, March*

**root word**                           a word that **prefixes** or **suffixes** can be added to, to make new words, e.g. *port, cycle could be made into report and recycle.*

**semi-colon**                          a punctuation mark (;) used to separate **clauses** or phrases in a sentence, e.g. *Kadir sold a large stereo; several DVDs; his collection of science fiction books and a mobile at the car boot sale.*

**simile**                                   where one thing is compared to another using the word as or like, e.g. *as old as the hills*

**subject**                               who or what a sentence is about, e.g. *Lisa sang a song.*

**subordinate clause**     used with a **main clause** in a sentence. A subordinate clause does not make sense on its own although it includes a **subject** and a **verb** and starts with a **connective**, e.g. *The hamsters were kept in their carry box while their cage was being cleaned.*

**suffix**                                  a group of letters added to the end of a word to alter its meaning, e.g. *less, ful, ly*

**synonym**                          a word with a similar meaning to another word, e.g. *large, huge*

**tense**                                  differing forms of a **verb** that reflect when actions take place, e.g. *in the present... I am going; in the past... I went; in the future... I will go*

**verb**                                    a doing or being word, e.g. *to jump, to understand*

# Progress grid

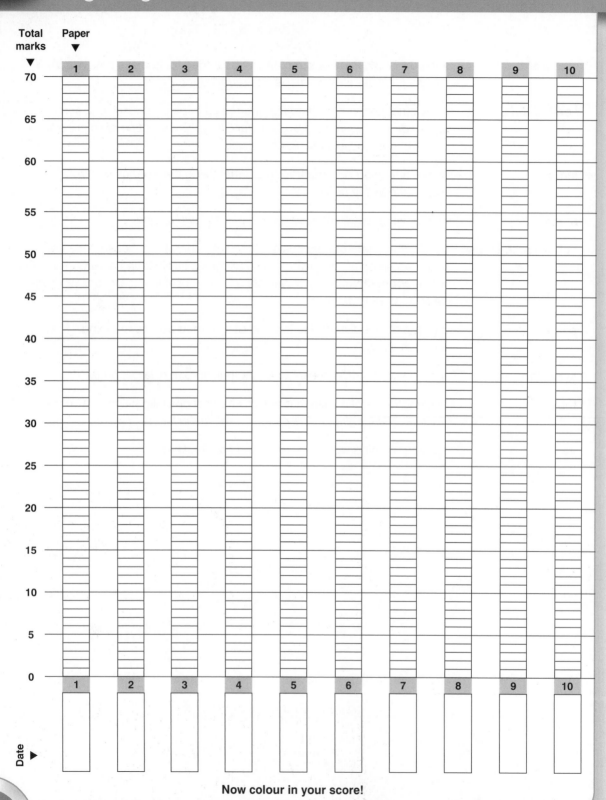

**Now colour in your score!**